Piano Exam Pieces

ABRSM Grade 4

Selected from the 2019 & 2020 syllabus

Name

Date of exam

© 2018 by The Associated Board of the Royal Schools of Music

Contents

page

Editor for ABRSM: Richard Jones

Other pieces for Grade 4

First published in 2018 by ABRSM (Publishing) Ltd,
a wholly owned subsidiary of ABRSM, 4 London Wall Place,
London EC2Y 5AU, United Kingdom
© 2018 by The Associated Board of the Royal Schools of Music
Distributed worldwide by Oxford University Press

Music origination by Julia Bovee
Cover by Kate Benjamin & Andy Potts, with thanks to Brighton College
Printed in England by Halstan & Co. Ltd, Amersham, Bucks.,
on materials from sustainable sources.
P14624

A:1

Bagatelle in C

WoO 54

Ludwig van Beethoven
(1770–1827)

Lustig [♪ = *c*.126]

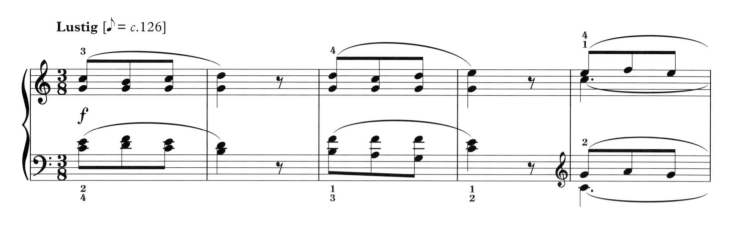

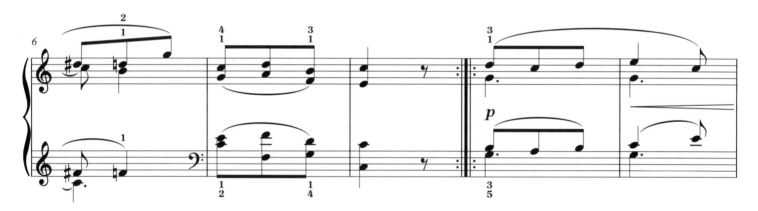

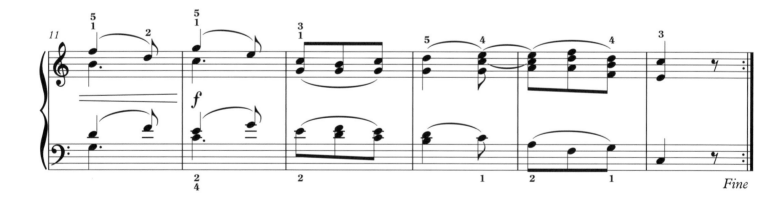

Fine

The *bagatelle* (French for 'trifle') is a short and intimate piano piece; Beethoven's well-known *Für Elise* is a good example of this. He wrote three collections of bagatelles, and many of his single piano pieces are similar to them in character, though not so called. This is true of the piece selected here (the title 'bagatelle' has been added by the editor), which was probably composed in the 1790s, when Beethoven was in his twenties, but not published till 1888. It is a *da capo* form piece (ABA), built on the contrast between cheerful (*lustig*) music in the major mode and sad (*traurig*) music in the minor.

Source: autograph MS, Staatsbibliothek zu Berlin, Preussischer Kulturbesitz, Nachlass Grasnick, 26. All dynamics are editorial suggestions only, as are all slurs in the *Minore* (minor-mode section).

© 1986 by The Associated Board of the Royal Schools of Music
Adapted from Beethoven: *Bagatelles*, edited by Howard Ferguson (ABRSM)

Traurig [Minore]

Sonatina in A minor

A:2

Georg Benda
(1722–95)

Benda's sonatinas are written in an early Classical style, like the sonatas of his contemporary C. P. E. Bach. The very polished, idiomatic Sonatina in A minor is designed in simple ritornello form. The tonic ritornello (bb. 1–16) is recapitulated at the end, as shown by the direction 'Da Capo al Fine'. In the middle, it occurs in the relative major C (bb. 25–32). The two episodes (bb. 17–24 and 33–48) both make use of hand-crossing technique – left hand: downstems; right hand: upstems.

Georg Benda, Bohemian by birth, settled in Germany as violinist in the Prussian court orchestra (1742–50), then in 1750 was appointed Capellmeister at the court of Gotha.

Source: *Sammlung vermischter Klavier- und Gesangstücke* (Gotha, 1781). The only original performance marks are *f* in b. 25 and the right-hand slurs and staccatos in bb. 41–3 and 47–8. All others are editorial suggestions only.

© 1987 by The Associated Board of the Royal Schools of Music
Adapted from Georg Benda: *Twelve Sonatinas*, edited by Richard Jones (ABRSM)

Little Game

Petit jeu

from *Fugues légères et petits jeux*

G. P. Telemann
(1681–1767)

Georg Philipp Telemann, an extremely prolific German composer, was city music director at Frankfurt (1712–21), then at Hamburg (1721–67). As a composer, he was versatile enough to turn his hand to all the different styles and genres of his day.

This piece is selected from a collection entitled *Fugues légères et petits jeux* (Light Fugues and Little Games), which is made up of six easy fugues, each accompanied by some shorter pieces in the same key. This playful A major piece is written in a dance style not unlike that of the polonaise.

Source: *Fugues légères et petits jeux* (Hamburg: author, 1737). All dynamics, slurs and staccatos are editorial suggestions only, with the exception of the staccato dots in bb. 10–11, which are present in the source.

B:1

The Reef

No. 5 from *In Southern Seas*

Walter Carroll
(1869–1955)

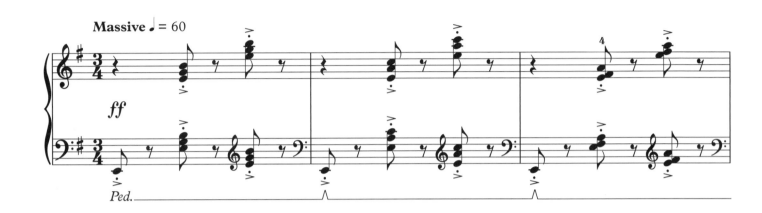

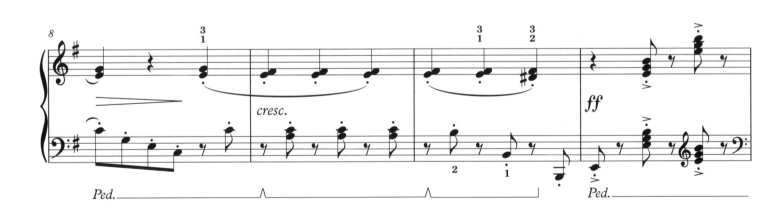

Walter Carroll was a Manchester-born music educator and composer who played a major role in the musical life of his native city. He wrote many piano works for students, including *In Southern Seas*, a set of nine miniature sound pictures with programmatic titles.

'The Reef' is prefaced by a motto from Thomas Blood: 'The great rock in the ocean stands/And battles with the waves for ever.' The *fortissimo* chords perhaps convey the immovable rock, whereas the *piano* episodes (bb. 5 and 15) might suggest the play of the waves on its jagged surface.

B:2

Arietta

No. 1 from *Lyriske småstykker*, Op. 12

Edvard Grieg
(1843–1907)

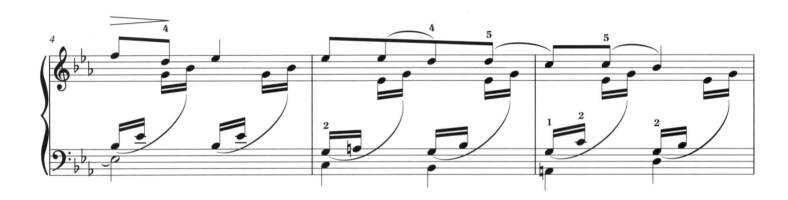

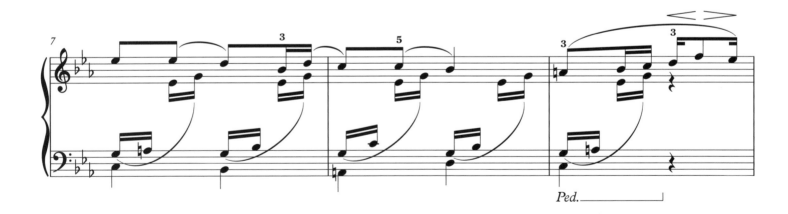

The Norwegian composer and pianist Edvard Grieg was adept at inventing miniature character-pieces for the piano, many of which were collected in his ten sets of *Lyriske småstykker* (Lyric Pieces), composed between 1867 and 1901.

The title 'arietta' is borrowed from opera, where it means 'little song'. Here, the melody is 'sung' by the piano at the top of the texture, accompanied by broken chords divided between the hands and a slow-moving bass.

© 1984 by The Associated Board of the Royal Schools of Music

Adapted from Grieg, *Lyric Pieces and Poetic Tone-Pictures*, Opp. 12 & 3, edited by Angus Morrison (ABRSM)

Morning Song

Chanson de matin

Op. 15 No. 2

B:3

Arranged by David Blackwell

Edward Elgar
(1857–1934)

In 1897 the English composer Edward Elgar published two pieces for violin sond piano, *Chanson de nuit* (Night Song) and *Chanson de matin* (Morning Song). Two years later, the first performance of his 'Enigma' Variations brought him fame, and he became widely recognized as the greatest English composer of his time.

Of the two violin pieces, *Chanson de matin* (arranged here for piano), with its exceptionally beautiful and memorable melody, has become particularly well known. A second tune enters in the left hand of b. 23 and is then taken over by the right hand (bb. 27 and 31).

Holiday in Paris

William Gillock
(1917–93)

William Gillock was an American music educator and composer of piano music, who lived and worked for many years in New Orleans, then later in the Dallas area. *Holiday in Paris* is written in ABA form, with a contrasting middle section (b. 16) between the two statements of the main theme (bb. 1 and 25), and a substantial coda (b. 45). Although the composer's metronome mark is ♩. = 66, students may prefer a more relaxed tempo, for example ♩. = c.54.

C:2

A Kwela for Caitlin

Richard Michael
(born 1949)

For the past 41 years, Scottish jazz musician Richard Michael has been teaching improvisation as director of Fife Youth Jazz Orchestra. He has since been involved in the development of ABRSM's jazz syllabus, and is honorary professor of jazz piano at St Andrews University.

About this piece, the composer has written: 'A kwela is a rhythmical style of popular African music, similar to jazz. This vibrant kwela, with its swung and offbeat quavers, often cut short by rests, has to groove! The tune goes from the light of D major into the dark of B minor – bring out that contrast and you've got it!'

© 2018 by The Associated Board of the Royal Schools of Music

Rhythmical

Rytmická

No. 6 from *Moments at the Piano*

Luboš Sluka
(born 1928)

The Czech composer Luboš Sluka studied at the Prague Conservatory and at the Academy of Performing Arts in the same city. He has written more than 350 compositions, including much film music.

This colourful and vivacious piece is a study in rhythm, as its title ('Rhythmical' in translation) indicates. Another significant feature of the piece is hand-crossing technique. The original contains no dynamics, so all the dynamics given here are editorial suggestions only.